Quake

Quake

ALEX KROPP

HIP Xtreme Novels

NATIONAL LIBRARY OF CANADA CATALOGUING IN PUBLICATION DATA

Kropp, Alex, 1979–
Quake / Alex Kropp.

ISBN 978-1-926847-23-8

I. Title.

PS8621.R66Q82 2012 jC813'.6 C2011-908541-0

General editor: Paul Kropp
Text Design: Laura Brady
Illustrations by: Charlie Hnatiuk
Cover design: Robert Corrigan

1 2 3 4 5 6 7 17 16 15 14 13 12

Printed and bound in Canada

High Interest Publishing acknowledges the financial support of the Government of Canada through the Canada Book Fund for our publishing activities.

Cyrus never took the earthquake threat seriously. But when the big quake hits, he acts fast to save his sister. It's the aftershock he wasn't ready to handle.

Contents

Chapter 1

Fault Line

"We're on a fault line, Cyrus. I tell you – it's just a matter of time." Evan was pointing with his finger. He did that to make me look up at him.

"Yeah, I know," I said.

It was lunch time. I was trying to eat a sandwich. Meanwhile Evan was going nuts.

Evan pushed his lunch to one side. "Look," he said to me. "Look at the map. Here's the fault line. Here's us." Now he was pointing his finger at the book.

"Yeah, right," I told him. "Here, eat one of these carrot sticks and try to calm down. The other kids are looking at us."

The other kids *were* looking at us. Of course, most

of the other kids thought we were weird, and maybe we were. I had that weird name – Cyrus. And I was born to an Asian dad and a white mom. So my face is a mix, half and half, and lots of kids think I'm Spanish.

Evan, on the other hand, is all white but really all weird. He's got wonky glasses and bad teeth. He collects strange comics and really likes 60s music. So if I'm weird, he's weird to the power of ten. And he worries too much.

"You're crazy," I told him.

"What?"

"You worry about stuff that you can't control," I said to him. "And that's crazy. Worry about the next math test, or something real."

"I'm just saying. . . ."

"And I'm just saying, keep your voice down. People are looking."

Of course, we really do live on a fault line. Our town is about four hours north of San Francisco. San Francisco is on the same fault line. Back in 1906, the land on each side of that fault line slipped a little. In two days, San Francisco was destroyed.

Since then, it hasn't been so bad. They say that we'll have an earthquake here every 22 years. That's the average. But the earthquake that was supposed to happen in 1993 didn't hit until 2004. So you never know.

Evan thinks the next earthquake will come soon. But I figure I'll be out of here before it hits. At least, I hope so.

There's not much to our town, really. There's an old movie theater, but that's closed. There's a couple of supermarkets and a Walmart. There's a hospital where my mom works. Then there's our high school, of course, but our teams always lose. The only remarkable thing about our school is Tracy McKinnon. Tracy McKinnon is gorgeous and sexy and just waiting for the break to get to Hollywood.

Of course Tracy McKinnon doesn't even know I exist. And she thinks that Evan is a kind of gross insect. Or so her friends say.

So if our whole town all went down in an earthquake . . . well, Tracy McKinnon would be the big loss. And maybe the Walmart. And maybe my kid sister, who's kind of cute even if she's really a goofy ten-year-old. But there's no sense worrying about it. That's what I keep telling Evan, but he's a bit crazy.

Evan says I have a thing for Tracy McKinnon that's

a bit crazy. So maybe we're even.

Later that day, we were in math class. Old Mr. Barnes was up front, doing some math on the white board. Tracy McKinnon was at one side of the classroom, simply looking beautiful. Evan was staring at his math book. And I was trying to think about math rather than . . . yeah, you guessed it.

Then the warning buzzer went off.

Old Mr. Barnes looked at his watch and groaned. "Earthquake drill," he told us. "Okay, let's DUCK."

DUCK is one of those stupid school words where each letter stands for something. D is for duck down on your knees. That's pretty simple. The floor starts shaking and you don't want to be standing up. U is to get under a desk, just in case the ceiling falls down on you. C is for cover your head. And K? I've forgotten K. It must be something like "keep calm." Always good advice.

So I was down on my knees, my head covered, when I heard Mr. Barnes.

"You, Kerner," he said. Bill Kerner was a mouthy kid in the class. Five years ago, he was the school bully. He used to like to pick on Evan and me. In fact, he still picks on Evan and me. "What part of DUCK don't you understand?"

"The D part, Mr. Barnes," Kerner replied. "I hurt my knees playing football, so it's hard to duck down. But I've got my head covered, see? I've got the C down perfect."

A bunch of the kids laughed. Mr. Barnes was not amused.

"Are you talking back to me, young man?"

"No sir," Bill Kerner replied. "I never talk back to teachers."

This got a little more laughing. Bill Kerner was a pretty snarky guy, and we all knew it.

"I'm just explaining my problem. Don't worry, sir. If the ceiling falls down, I'll be fine."

Another round of laughing, but Mr. Barnes let it go.

"Okay, let's move out. Take the route to the parking lot. Cyrus, you take the Disaster Folder. Let's go."

So we all got up and began moving out. Bill Kerner was joking with his buddies. Tracy McKinnon was smiling at him. And I had to put up the green card that says our classroom is all clear. Great, I thought.

So we all got to the back parking lot. The gym teacher brought out the "Disaster Cart," which looks like a rolling garbage can. Nobody knows what's inside. A bunch of guys put on T-shirts that said "Search and Rescue Team." But there was never a real earthquake. There was nobody to search for. Nobody to rescue. It all seemed kind of stupid.

That's what I told Evan.

"You can't say that," he shot back. "We've all got to be ready. Like those people in Japan in 2011. They were ready, and that saved hundreds of thousands of people."

"Well, yeah, I guess."

"You can't just joke about this, Cyrus. It's going to happen. Sooner or later, a real earthquake is going to hit us."

Which is when Bill Kerner came over beside us. He reached out with both hands and began shaking Evan like crazy.

"Wha-wha-what are you-you do-doing?" Evan asked.

Bill Kerner laughed and his football buddies joined in. "Just getting you ready for the big quake, Evan. Now you know what the shaking will feel like. Want to put your hands up on your head and see if it helps?"

Chapter 2 Warnings

So did the quake happen that night? That's what you're wondering. That's how the TV movie would go. But there was no earthquake that night, or that week, or that month. Evan kept on moaning and groaning, but nothing happened.

It wasn't until two months later that we got a shake. A little shake.

We live in a little three-storey building, up on the top floor. There are only six units, so it's not a really tall building. But it's tall for our town.

I was getting ready for school at the crack of dawn – about seven, I guess. I was in the kitchen putting some Wheaties into a bowl. Then I walked

over to the fridge to get some milk . . . and something happened. My feet began moving a little, in a funny way, and I heard some dishes rattle. It was pretty quiet. There was no big roar, just a little tinkle of sound.

My mom was in the shower. I don't think she noticed a thing. My little sister was still asleep. She didn't wake up. I began to wonder if it was just me. But then I got a text from Evan:

<its a quake. a four. did you feel it>

Me: <yeah, felt it. kinda a tickle that's all>

<its a warning. watch out for the aftershock>

Me: <remember to duck. lol>

But the little quake made the news. Nothing was really damaged. There were no buildings that fell down, no roads sticking up in the air. The TV news guys talked about it, though. A few hundred people called the cops. One old lady lost a fancy teapot. And they said it was a 4 on the Richter scale.

Around here, we all know the Richter scale. It tells you how bad an earthquake is on a scale of 1 to 10. Up to a 3, nothing happens that people can see. (Dogs and cats are more aware of it.) At 4, everything shakes a little but there's no damage. At 5, junky buildings crack and you can really feel the shake. At 6, things get bad. For a hundred miles from the earthquake center, buildings fall down. At 7 and 8, it's like a Hollywood disaster film. The San Francisco earthquake was an 8, and the whole city was destroyed.

At 9 on the Richter scale, everything goes down. The Japan earthquake of 2011 was a 9. More than 30,000 people died – and they were ready for the quake. But they weren't ready for the tidal wave that came after.

It's like I always tell Evan – you can't worry about earthquakes. You can try to be ready, but you can't worry about them.

Of course, Evan is super ready. I think his parents are as crazy as he is. They've got an "Earthquake Prep Kit" ready to go. There's drinking water, food, first aid stuff, money, passports. The whole kit is in a rolling suitcase that's ready to go . . . except there'd be nowhere to go. We only have three roads out of town, and they'd be blocked. So the kit is supposed to keep them alive until help comes.

We talked about the little earthquake when we got to school.

"That's just the first one," Evan said. "There are more to come."

"How do you know?"

"My dad says. He says that earthquakes come in groups. There's no surprise, just that people don't pay attention."

Evan's dad is an old hippy farmer. He's a bit nuts.

"Is that so?"

"My dad says there's a p-wave that comes before an earthquake. It gives you a warning."

"How much warning?" I asked him.

"I don't know for sure. Maybe a couple of minutes. In Calistoga, it sets off a siren."

"What about here?"

Evan shook his head. "Here? We don't even have a good pizza joint."

So Evan was getting to me. At school, we called him Bad News Evan. The kids made fun of him – even I made fun of him. But at home, I looked up p-waves and earthquake science. The truth is, nobody can predict an earthquake. A p-wave might give you two minutes' warning, but nobody knows when a quake will hit. Nobody knows how big it will be.

If you're lucky, you never find out.

But we weren't so lucky.

It was early morning at our house, a nice June day coming up – or so the TV said. I was pouring milk onto my Wheaties. Mom had gone off early to her job at the hospital. My dad was out of town, working on the east coast. And my sister was still in bed. She's the princess in this house, so she gets to sleep in most days.

Then we had a little shake, a tremor. It was like the last one, only a little bigger. All the glasses and dishes in the kitchen shook. The floor moved under me just a little. The lights blinked on and off. And that was that. There wasn't any sound. Nothing broke. It was just a little tremor.

But it woke my sister up. "Cyrus," she yelled from her bedroom. "What was that?"

"A tremor!" I shouted back. "It's nothing."

"I could feel the bed move," she shouted.

"That's why they call it a tremor. Things move a little."

"But I'm scared," she whined. "Is mom still home?"

"Gone to work."

"So can you come here? I'm scared."

My sister Rachel is ten. At age ten, she should be used to a little tremor now and then. It's not as if we've never had them before. But Rachel is still scared of spiders and ghosts and now a little earth tremor.

"Yeah, yeah. I'm coming."

I walked down the hall to her bedroom with my bowl of Wheaties. When I opened the door, Rachel was sitting in her bed with her hands over her head.

"What are you doing?" I asked her.

"Like they tell us at school. I've covered my head," she explained.

I took a spoonful of my cereal. "Just in case the ceiling comes down."

"Right," she said.

"So you don't really need me," I told her.

"Cyrus," she whined, "I'm scared."

"What am I going to do?" I asked her. "Hold up the ceiling?"

Rachel made a face at me. I think she was going to say something, too. She was looking for some snappy come-back. But she had no time to find it. She had no time to do anything.

Neither did I. Because that's when the earthquake hit.

Chapter 3 The Quake

First five seconds

The sound came first. There was a deep, deep roar – like an explosion. But bigger. Think of the big, boomy bass that you get at a rock concert. Or think of thunder just outside your window. Boom. Then multiply that by a hundred.

The sound was so big, so deep, that I didn't hear it. I felt it. I felt it blasting my skin and my body. I felt it blowing my eardrums.

Then things started to move. Everything shook. Things began shaking so fast it seemed crazy. Rachel's toys and dolls were all shaking. So was all the girlie

stuff on her dresser. The shaking went into my body, like a tingle. The outside world was shaking, and I was tingling and already deaf.

Then the floor rose up. It was like a giant fist under the floor had punched it. Suddenly the floor was going up two, three feet.

And I went with it. The floor had been punched and I'd been punched with it. The bowl of cereal in my hand went flying. The spoon went flying. Then the milk and Wheaties were falling upward – I know that sounds stupid, but that's how it was. I had the sense that I was falling, but falling upward.

Next ten seconds

When I was able to hear again, I heard my sister screaming. There was her high-pitched scream. There was a deep rumble all around us. And there was the sound of things breaking – cracking, twisting.

"Rach – " I yelled.

I was going to tell her that it was an earthquake. A big one. But that seemed dumb. Of course it was an earthquake. My sister didn't need me to tell her that.

Then I was going to say that everything would be all right. But I wasn't sure about that. And my voice was all weird, like words couldn't come out.

But I did something smart.

I grabbed my sister while we were both up in the air. She only weighs about 70 pounds, so grabbing her was easy. Then we both fell down on the bed in a heap. Everything fell down, making a tremendous crash.

Rachel had stopped screaming. She was too scared.

So was I, but somehow I kept thinking. I thought about how we were going to survive the next minute. That was my goal. Survive another 45 seconds.

"Under!" I shouted.

I grabbed Rachel and pulled her off the bed. Then I shoved her under it. That was the easy part. The hard part was sliding under the bed beside her. I'm a lot bigger than she is, and the bed is pretty small. And things were still moving – not up and down, but kind of sideways. Still, I got under the bed, somehow.

Rachel was crying.

That made a lot of sense to me, too. If I'd been any good at crying, I think I would have done it too. Instead, I just got all tensed up, wondering what would happen next. We were on the third floor of a building.

If the whole building went down. . . .

Next fifteen seconds

So I was thinking about the building collapsing. That was the picture in my mind. But the next sound I heard was a giant craaack. I waited, and then there was a sound like thunder, and then the air turned white.

I'm dead, I thought. The white light meant I was going to Heaven. Isn't that what they say – you see a white light in the second before you die?

But then Rachel started coughing. And I had trouble breathing. It took a second to figure it out. But if I could still hear and still breathe, I couldn't be dead.

I tried to move, but the bed was pressing down on me. The air was full of white dust, like a bag of flour had just exploded.

"Rachel, are you okay?" I said.

"It hurts," she said. Then she started crying and coughing again.

"It'll be okay," I told her. There, I got out my big line. I had no idea if it was true. I had no idea what would happen next. But it seemed to be the right thing to say.

I pushed up on the bed, but it was really heavy. It felt like some giant were sitting on top of it. So I looked to one side and saw what had happened. The ceiling had fallen down. There was plaster and plaster dust everywhere.

That was a relief. A ceiling coming down – well, that wasn't too bad. It was bad, but not that bad.

So what do we do now? I asked myself. I got this picture in my head of our building going down. "We get out of here," I said, maybe out loud.

Next thirty seconds

"C'mon," I said to Rachel. "We've gotta move."

"But I can't," she whined.

"We've got to."

I wiggled sideways beneath the bed. I kept holding onto Rachel's hand, and that made it harder to move. First I got my feet out from under the bed, and then my butt. But I had to let go of Rachel's hand to push the rest of me out.

"Okay, come on," I said, reaching under. "Hold my hand and I'll pull you."

So I kind of dragged my sister from under the bed. Her arms and head came out first, then her feet. She was still in her pink PJs, but now she was all covered with white dust. It was the same dust that was clogging my nose.

I had to reach up and blow my nose into my hand. The snot came out white, with a little bit of blood.

"Okay, let's get out of here," I said.

But Rachel didn't want to move. She was just staring around her bedroom – or what used to be her bedroom.

It was a disaster. The ceiling was gone. We could see sunlight through holes in the roof. Everything on the walls or on shelves had fallen down. Everything on the floor was covered with white dust and pieces of glass. There were no working lights and the window had blown out.

"My dolls," Rachel cried.

"We'll come back and get them later," I told her.

"But Cy. . . ."

"We'll come back," I repeated. "Trust me."

Chapter 4

Escape

I gave Rachel her coat and shoes, since she was only in PJs. Then I grabbed mine and looked for my cell phone. It was plugged into the charger. Then I grabbed a few dollars from the dish in the kitchen and got ready to go.

But the hall door was stuck.

"Push," Rachel said.

"I tried," I told her. "I think the whole building is at an angle. You stand back."

I took a running jump at the door, leading with my shoulder. There was a smash, and then it flew open. That was the good part. The bad part was that my shoulder hurt like crazy.

The outside hall was dark. All the lights were out, and the one window didn't give much light. The floor was covered with plaster and broken glass.

"Hey, is everybody okay?" I shouted.

There was no answer. Our floor had only four units, so maybe all the others had left. Maybe nobody else was home when the quake hit.

"What about Mrs. Hardy?" Rachel asked.

Mrs. Hardy was a real old lady who lived next to us. Sometimes she complained about the noise we made, but she wasn't a real old bag. She was just old. So I went and knocked on her door.

"Mrs. Hardy, are you in there?" I shouted.

Again, no answer. I wondered if she'd gotten under something – before the ceilings fell down. But I tried not to picture it. I tried the handle, but the door was locked.

"Can't you break down the door?" Rachel asked.

"That's only on TV," I told her. "Besides, I already messed up my shoulder. Once is enough."

So we made our way down the hall, stepping over big chunks of plaster and stuff from the roof. At the stairs, we could hear noise from outside. There were sirens. There were people shouting and some crying.

And all the car alarms in the area were sounding off.

Going down the stairs was strange. The stairs were all at a funny angle, and some of them were bent. Down at the first floor, a couple of stairs were gone altogether. But Rachel and I made it okay. Then we got through the lobby and out onto the street.

"Holy ——!" I swore. I try not to swear in front of my sister, but there was nothing else to say. It was a disaster like I couldn't imagine.

The street was buckled down the middle. Every window was smashed. The sign on the corner store had fallen down. Cars were thrown around the street like they were toys tossed by a giant. In the distance, I could see smoke from a dozen fires.

Then there were people. It seemed like everyone was out on the street, waiting for something to happen. Some people were white-faced, some scared, some hurt. People walked or stumbled around like zombies from a movie. But there was nobody in charge. Nobody seemed to know what to do.

"Cyrus," I heard from down the street.

I knew the voice – Evan. Bad News Evan. After all these months of waiting for an earthquake, he got one. A bigger one that anyone would have predicted.

I waited with my sister until Evan reached our place. He was walking with a kind of limp, with a rolling suitcase beside him.

"You gotta move," he yelled. "Don't stand in front of a tall building."

I looked at our apartment block. Three storeys high didn't make a tall building.

"What?" I shouted.

Evan was out of breath by then. "If there's an aftershock, the front of the building can fall off. Or the whole thing might collapse. So get to the middle of the street. It's the safest."

So we moved. Maybe I had made fun of Evan, but he knew more than I did.

"Where are your parents?" I asked him.

"They were driving to work," he said. "Now they could be anywhere, they could be alive or dead. All of us. . . ."

I just shook my head. He talked as if it didn't matter much. Then I thought about my mom who was already at work at the hospital. The seven-storey tall hospital.

So I changed the subject. "What's in the suitcase?"

"The survival kit," Evan said. "Good for three days. Water. Flashlights. Food. A radio."

"You're dragging three days worth of water up a hill?" I asked.

"Yeah, we're going to need it," he said. "Everything's gone out. No gas. No electricity. No water. We're going to be on our own until help comes."

"When are we gonna get help?" my sister piped up.

"Don't know," Evan told her. "The cell phones don't work. The land lines don't work. And the radio is all about the big cities. San Francisco was hit hard. So was Seattle. The whole west coast has gone nuts."

"So what do we do?" I asked him. "If your parents made an emergency kit, they must have made some kind of plan."

"Yeah, we're supposed to call my uncle in San Francisco. But there's no phones working. And then we're supposed to meet at the closest school. Anyhow, that's the plan."

"Okay, so Rachel's school is the closest. Let's go."

It made sense, really. Her school was only two blocks away. Somebody there would know what to do. They were ready for this kind of thing.

So we turned and started walking up the hill. Other people started following us. It seemed like no one had a better idea.

We weren't very far down the block when I heard a "pop" back behind us. I turned and looked down the street. There was one more "pop" and then suddenly there was an explosion. It was our building. A ball of flame shot out of the front lobby. There were cracking sounds as the front of the building began to crumble.

"Cy, what is it?" my sister asked.

"Nothing," I told her. "Just a car. Nothing to worry

about."

So I kept pushing her forward, pushing her so she couldn't look back. I tried hard not to look back myself. But when we turned the corner toward the school, I looked over my shoulder.

Our building was a mass of flames. A gas explosion, I figured. And there'd be nothing left.

"Hey, man. I told you," Evan said. "Good thing I got you moving away from that place."

I suppose I could have said thanks. Or maybe I could have counted us lucky. But I didn't. All I could do was swear – for the second time that morning.

Chapter 5
Safe?

Rachel's school looked fine. I guess they built the place so an earthquake wouldn't knock it down. Of course, it was only two storeys tall. It wasn't like some high-rise that might fall right over. It was a school, a small school with a few broken windows.

There were lots of people going inside. It was like voting day – all sorts of adults going into school. This time, of course, they weren't going to vote. They were going to stay alive.

Schools are good for emergencies. Lots of them are set up with extra water and food – just in case. And some of the teachers know first aid, or they've got some kind of training. I guess they go to courses to learn about disasters, just like we learn math and English.

"We should be okay now," I said to Evan.

"Maybe," Evan replied. Bad News Evan was back.

"What do you mean, maybe?"

"You ever heard of afterschocks?"

"Aftershocks," I repeated. It wasn't a question. I knew what they were.

Evan shook his head. "The aftershock can be worse than the earthquake. The quake we had, they say it was a 7.5 or an 8. But the aftershock can be a 6 or a 9. If it's a 9, we're all toast."

"Are you always so cheerful?"

"I'm just saying. . . ."

Evan was cut off when Rachel ran up ahead. She had found a friend, some girl I didn't know. The friend had a mom and a few more kids Rachel's age. It looked like some ten-year-old's birthday party. All the little girls were laughing and talking like crazy. So was Rachel. She didn't know, yet, that we had no place to go back to.

"This way – this way," shouted one of the teachers. "Everyone move to the gym, please. Just keep moving forward."

The gym made sense. No windows. No real ceiling, just the metal of the roof. Not much that could fall down, really. The lights up there have to survive us throwing basketballs at them, so they're pretty secure. Of course, those lights didn't work. Nothing really worked. But the emergency lights were on. And there was a sense of order that we didn't have on the street.

The teachers had us grouped by streets. All the people from my street went to one spot, all the people from other streets had their spots. Evan went off to his subdivision. Rachel and her friends were mostly from our area.

It looked like the school was ready for the long haul. There were gym mats ready to become beds. There were big barrels of water for people who were thirsty. (I went over there in a hurry.) And there was a first aid station for people who were hurt.

A lot of people were hurt. The school nurse and a couple of teachers were putting on bandages and splints, but that was all they could do. This wasn't a hospital, just a school. People who needed a hospital – they were still waiting for help. It would be a long wait.

Until help came.

"You know, in Japan, they had to wait four days for help." It was Evan, of course. He had checked in with his group and come over to bug us. "No heat, no power, no water – for four days. Think about it."

"Evan, I don't want to think about it," I told him. "We're okay. We're going to get through this. My sister is even having a good time. It's like some kind of lame party for the pre-teen set."

"Yeah, but she doesn't know yet, does she?" Evan snapped back. "She didn't see your apartment building."

"No," I said.

"And what about your mom?" Evan asked.

"She's at the hospital," I said. "That place is built like a tank."

"It's over seven storeys tall," Evan replied. "That's a big building for a big earthquake. And what if a gas pipe broke? There might be fire . . . there might be anything."

That's when I lost it. I mean, it had been a pretty tough day, and now this. "Evan, would you shut up!" There was a swear word in there, too. My third for the day.

"I'm just saying. . . ."

I shot him a look.

Evan took out his Walkman radio and gave me one earbud. I guess he was trying to be friends again, so I took it.

On the radio we got the news:

A major earthquake rocked the west coast this morning. There was damage to buildings in San Francisco and Seattle. The center of the quake was 120 miles northeast of San Francisco in the small town of . . .

That was us. We were the center – the epicenter – of the earthquake. And it was a very big quake: 7.6 on the Richter scale. That was bad enough to cause damage to the big cities more than 100 miles away. In our town, it lifted roads and knocked down buildings. We used to have a city hall. Now it was a pile of steel and rubble. We used to have a big church. Now it was a pile of stone.

On TV, we would have had pictures. On radio, we could only listen. There were reporters in the big cities talking about small damage. Yeah, the Golden Gate Bridge moved and the skyscrapers on First Street all tilted. But nothing fell down. No building fronts just collapsed – like ours did. Nobody died.

But in our town, we only had one reporter. Things sounded really awful. Buildings had collapsed. People were trapped. Roads were destroyed. Gas fires were burning. Part of the hospital had fallen down.

I looked up at nothing. My mom. Was my mom all right?

"Hey, they didn't say anybody got hurt," Evan told me.

"Right," I said. I felt like my throat had gone dry as dust.

Then there was a strange silence. Evan didn't know what else to say. Neither did I . . . for a while. And then I got an idea.

"Let's go outside and look up the hill," I said. The hospital was up the hill. We couldn't see much of it, but we could see something. "Maybe . . . maybe we can see something."

Evan nodded. I went over to tell my sister that I was going outside. She paid no attention. Then Evan and I left the dark gym.

Chapter 6
Aftershock

Our town is in a valley, right beside a river. The school is halfway up a hill. The hospital is almost at the top. From outside the school, we could see both down and up.

The town, down below, looked . . . flat. We never had many big buildings, but any buildings we had were down. We could see the pile that used to be city hall. Another pile was the big church. Another pile was the TV station. There were fire trucks and emergency vehicles all over town. Their lights flashed, some sirens still blared. In a few places, fires were still burning.

"Pretty bad," Evan said.

"Yeah," I agreed.

"If this were San Francisco, it would be worse."

"Yeah. And it would be all over the news."

"We're still all over the news. Kind of a lousy way to get famous," Evan replied.

I didn't answer. Instead I turned and looked up the hill. There was the hospital. My mom was an X-ray tech and she worked on the third floor. It looked like the whole building was fine. Maybe some small garage had fallen down, but not the hospital.

"Looks good," Evan said. He had followed my eyes up the hill. "For a big earthquake, we came out okay."

"So far," I said.

"So far?"

"Yeah, you know about aftershocks, don't you? I mean, you know all about disasters."

And then, I swear, we felt it.

There was a noise like a jet engine, then a rumble, and then the land began to move. It's so weird. One second you're standing on solid ground; the next second and its all moving. You feel like you're moving or falling, but it's really the ground. Everything moves. You just try to keep your balance.

Or not. I was okay for a couple of seconds, then I

went flying down. Or maybe the ground came flying up. I'm still not sure. I think the ground was moving for ten or twenty seconds. It felt like the ground was alive, like some kind of giant animal. I was trying to ride a giant horse with no saddle . . . and I got thrown. The next thing I knew, I was down on the ground, looking at grass. I rolled and saw Evan on the ground nearby. He was groaning.

I tried to sit up, but things were still moving. Or

maybe my head was spinning.

Maybe two minutes later, it was over. Evan and I were both sitting up. The school beside us was just fine. No more damage. No real danger to my sister or anybody inside.

But up the hill, things weren't so good.

When I looked at the hospital, I saw something was wrong. There's a metal awning – a portico – that goes out over the driveway. It keeps you from getting wet when it rains. But the portico was down. Collapsed. And it looked like the hospital had a crack right in the middle.

Then it all got worse. I felt like it was all in slow motion, like when the twin towers went down in New York. First there was this crack. Then the roof over the crack began to fall in. And then the two sides of the building began to fall toward the middle.

I could see the windows moving toward each other, the roof falling, the sides collapsing in. There was smoke or steam or something coming up.

And it was all in silence. The hospital was too far away for us to hear a thing.

"Sh—" Now it was Evan's turn to swear.

I couldn't say anything. I sat there, my mouth wide

open, staring.

Mom! But the word was in my head, not in my mouth.

When my mouth could move again, I said, "We've got to get up there."

"What?" Evan replied.

"We've got to get up there. My mom's up there."

"You're crazy," Evan told me. "One more aftershock and the whole hospital might come down. There's nothing you can do."

I shot him a look. Then I got up and ran back to the school.

Chapter 7
Volunteers

The principal was in the hall when I got inside. Evan showed up right behind me.

"The hospital. . . ." I said, not sure how to go on.

"We know," the principal said. "There was a call on the satellite phone. Now we're looking for some volunteers to go up there. Some of the teachers are going. . . ."

"And the two of us," I said brightly. "We can help. I know the hospital like the back of my hand. My mom works there and. . . ."

He gave me a long look, checking me up and down. "How old are you, son?" he asked.

"Sixteen," I lied. "So is my friend."

"I guess that's old enough," he sighed. "Go see Mr. Wu over there. He's taking the volunteers up the hill."

I could see Mr. Wu talking to a few other teachers. He was my sister's science teacher. He'd taught me science, too, five years ago. We used to call him Wacky Wu because . . . well, just because.

Evan tugged at my shirt sleeve. "We're not sixteen," he whispered.

"We're almost sixteen," I whispered back. "Wacky hasn't got time to figure out how old we are."

So we walked over beside the teachers. Mr. Wu remembered me, and maybe Evan. As I guessed, he didn't ask how old we were. He just added us to the group. There were four teachers and the two of us. Mr. Wu gave us flashlights and gloves from the supplies at the school. Then he took us out to his Jeep.

I think Jeeps hold four people, at least most of the time. For seven of us to fit in, we really had to squeeze. Evan ended up behind the back seat, wedged sideways. The rest of us crowded together as Mr. Wu put the old Jeep into gear. Then we bounced up the road toward the hospital. Most days, it takes ten minutes – max. But not today. There were a hundred cars heading up the hill, and a bunch of cars that were simply left beside the road. And none of them were going anywhere.

That's when Mr. Wu swore. I guess he forgot that we were in the Jeep. Or maybe teachers swear a lot when they're not in class. Anyhow, Mr. Wu steered his Jeep off to the side of the road. Then he started zooming around cars and trees and broken pavement. I always wondered if Jeeps could really do off-road. That day, I found out.

The only problem was inside. We kept bouncing side to side as Mr. Wu drove. It felt like a crazy amusement park ride, or maybe Crazy Taxi in real life. But it worked. While the cars on the road were stuck, we kept moving forward.

In fifteen minutes we were at the hospital. And the hospital was a mess. A wing at the back had fallen down. The front canopy had crashed. And the whole building was leaning in on itself, the middle of it sagging.

The parking lot was already full of people. There were hospital staff. There were patients still in hospital gowns. There were a few people on stretchers and in wheelchairs. But for a hospital with 700 patients, there sure weren't 700 people.

"Okay," Mr. Wu told us, "the job is simple. We've

got to get sick people out of the building before it goes down. One more aftershock and it's all over. If you feel something coming, get out before you get killed yourself."

I looked over at Evan. He seemed white-faced and maybe sick.

"There's got to be somebody in charge out there. Do what they say. Do what the doctors and nurses tell you. And move fast. The way that building looks, we don't have a lot of time."

The six of us got out and tried to decide where to go. The front doors were useless, blocked by the wrecked steel of the canopy. But a bunch of people seemed to be going in and out of the east doors.

"Over there," I said, pointing the way. "There are doors and stairs that go all the way up."

Mr. Wu gave me a look.

"My mother works here," I said. "I kind of know the building."

"Okay, let's move," Mr. Wu shouted, and we began running toward the doors. Somebody there told us to go in and up one floor, so we did it.

That's when I saw Hell. I'm not kidding. If there were a Hell on earth, it was on the second floor of that hospital.

It was the sound of Hell that came first. Moaning, coughing, crying.

Then came the sight of it. Under the dim emergency lights, it was a disaster. Walls were crashed and the ceiling had fallen down. The hallways were a mess of carts and wheelchairs and people.

And the people were the worst. All of them were hurt, some of them hurt bad. There were people with broken arms, people with smashed faces. Everywhere there was blood.

"You guys new?" asked somebody.

"Yeah," Mr. Wu said.

"Go down the hall and check this floor. Bring anybody you find down here. Unplug them, carry them or wheel them. It doesn't matter. Get 'em here."

We were on it.

We followed Mr. Wu down the hall to the 2J wing. The air was thick with dust and smoke.

"This the end of the floor?" Mr. Wu asked me.

"It's the middle," I told him. "But the center part has fallen down, so it's as far as we can go."

"Okay, let's spread out and rescue these guys," Mr. Wu shouted.

Evan and I went into 2J4, a double room. There were two old guys in there. One was lying on a bed with a couple of tubes running into his arm. He seemed okay. The other old man was just crying to himself.

"We've got to get you out of here," I told them. "Can either of you walk?"

There was no answer. In the corner of the room, there was a single wheelchair. I figured the guy on the IV was worse off, so he'd get the wheelchair. One of us could bring the IV bags. Evan and I got next to the bed to lift him. I'd seen my mom do this, like a dozen times, so I knew it wasn't that hard. Evan was just clueless.

"I'll reach under his legs; you get his shoulders. Ready . . . lift."

The lift wasn't pretty, but it worked. We got the one old guy in the wheelchair, and Evan hooked up his IV feeds again.

Then I went over to the other old guy, the crying one.

"Sir, I'm going to help you down the hall. We have to get you out of the hospital."

The answer I got didn't make any sense. The guy

was crying and blubbering and saying nothing at all.

"Okay, here we go," I said, pulling off the blankets and moving his legs to one side. "Can you walk, sir?"

He didn't answer. But when I got his feet on the ground, his whole body went limp. This guy wasn't walking anywhere.

"Well, sir. It looks like you get full service," I said. Then I lifted him in both arms and started for the door. "Let's go," I told Evan.

The old guy didn't weigh much, but after a couple of minutes it got tough to carry him. Of course, Evan wasn't doing all that well with the wheelchair. The floor was a mess of cracked plaster and heaved floor tiles. Still, we made our way through. I could see Mr. Wu carrying an old guy up ahead of me. And the other teachers were pushing people in wheelchairs.

We finally got them all to the room where we started. Other volunteers would get them down the stairs. It was our job to head back into the building and get more people.

"Hey, Cyrus," Mr. Wu told me. "You did a pretty good job back there."

"You, too, sir," I told him.

We raced back down the hall, taking a right turn

halfway. I knew it would take us to the emergency room. Or what was left of the emergency room.

I figured the place would be in bad shape. It was near the center of the building, so it might have collapsed. But the room wasn't that awful. It was the people in it. They must have come up to the hospital after the first quake. And now they were caught by the aftershock – some of them trapped.

I stopped and looked around. Some people were stuck under chunks of ceiling. Others, the lucky ones, were shaking, crying and moaning.

And then I heard my name. "Cyrus, help me."

Chapter 8 A Special Victim

I followed the sound. The voice came again, "Cyrus, over here."

That's when I saw him. It was Bill Kerner, or the face of Bill Kerner. The rest of him, his body, was buried under a section of ceiling that had collapsed.

"You gotta get me out of here," he said.

"Why, what happened?"

"I got caught by the first quake . . ." he said, each word hurting him. "Broke my arm. Now I'm trapped here. . . . If you can. . . ."

I didn't know what to do. I mean, I knew Bill Kerner – even if I didn't like the guy that much. And maybe I could get him out, somehow. But I didn't really know how.

"Let me get some help," I told him. Then I went over to Mr. Wu, who seemed to be in charge.

"Mr. Wu," I said, "I know that guy over there. He's stuck, but he's not hurt bad."

"How do you know?" he asked.

"Well, I'm just guessing," I said. "But he needs help."

"So do the other twenty people here," Mr. Wu shot back. "And we can get them out right away. Your buddy will have to wait."

"But. . . ."

"We're fighting against time, Cyrus. Your buddy can wait."

I felt bad. I couldn't look over at Bill Kerner. I didn't go back to explain. I knew that Mr. Wu was right, that we couldn't waste time on one person. There might be hundreds of people still trapped in the hospital. Most of those could get out with a little help. Getting Bill Kerner free from the rubble could take a long time.

So I got a woman into a wheelchair and raced down the hall. And then I remembered a word: triage. It's French. In a disaster, it's the toughest word.

Triage is when you figure out who lives and who dies.

You divide people who are hurt into three groups. The ones who are going to die, you leave behind. The ones who need help right away, they get help first. The ones in between, they just have to wait.

Bill Kerner wasn't going to get help right away. Mr. Wu figured he was going to die anyhow. There was no sense wasting time on him.

A tough call. But we were making a lot of tough calls. There was one old lady who wouldn't move. I tried to put her in a wheelchair, and she struggled against me. I tried again and she hit me.

So I left her behind. I moved a pregnant woman who was breathing hard. I moved a guy who had lost one arm. I moved two people who seemed kind of stunned.

We were doing pretty well. There was a system to get people to the second floor lobby. Then a group would carry them downstairs. Outside, there were helicopters for people who had to get to another hospital fast. And there were beds and tents and people to help.

Inside, it was still Hell. The work we were doing was crazy and disorganized and dirty. I won't even tell you about the worst stuff – the blood, the bedpans, the smells. You can just try to imagine.

We finally got the emergency room clear. Clear except for Bill Kerner. He was still stuck under the fallen ceiling. Moaning. Crying. Calling my name.

"Cyrus, you can't leave me here," he cried.

"I'm not in charge, Bill."

"Yeah, but you know me. You know I've got to get out of here."

"There are a lot of people who are hurting," I told him. "We've only got so much time."

"Yeah, but I'm hurting too," he moaned. "If you can just get this stuff off me, I'll be okay. I'll get out of here."

I looked over at the fallen ceiling. The problem was, the ceiling wasn't just plaster. There were metal pieces, and wire cable, and some kind of sharp plastic. All of that had fallen on Bill, and maybe some pieces were sticking into him. The odds weren't good.

"It's too heavy to lift," I told him. I'd tried that once.

"Get some help," he said. "Isn't that Evan over there?"

"You used to say that Evan was a wimp."

"Well, forget that," Bill replied. "Maybe the two of you?" He was begging me. I could hear it in his voice.

Meanwhile Mr. Wu was pointing upstairs. It was time for us to move on. My mom might be up on the third floor. She might need my help.

But here was Bill Kerner, right in front of me. The guy had been cruddy to me most of my life, but now he was in trouble. So maybe he was worth five minutes.

"Evan," I called over. "Come and give me a hand."

Evan came over. He was looking pretty bad himself. His face was white and he'd cut his arm so there was blood all over his clothes. As soon as he got near me, he knew it was Bill Kerner stuck under the wall.

"We gotta get upstairs," he said. He wouldn't even look at Bill.

"Yeah, but maybe we can get Bill out of this," I said. Then I started coughing. There was a lot of dust in the air. "See that piece of wood?" I said. "I'm going to wedge it beside him and lift. If the ceiling goes up, you pull him out. Okay?"

"We're supposed to be going," Evan repeated.

"Just one try," I said. "We'll give it one try."

Evan grunted. Bill said something like thanks. I went to one side and picked up a piece of wood, a 2x4, about eight feet long. I could use it like a lever, maybe, to lift up the fallen ceiling. It was the only chance Bill Kerner had. Maybe it was worth one try.

So I pushed the wood in beside him, leaving about half of it outside as a wedge. I pushed up to see if the wedge lifted a little, and it did.

"Ready?" I asked Evan.

He didn't answer, but I was ready. So I got crouched under the wood and lifted with my whole body. The fallen ceiling began creaking. Something inside it was breaking. But slowly I could lift it up – just a little at first, then a space the width of my arm.

"Pull him," I yelled. "I can't keep this up forever."

Evan pulled.

And Bill Kerner screamed. He gave out a scream like I'd never heard before. And I never want to hear it again. Not ever.

Evan shined his flashlight into the space I'd made above Bill. Then he swore.

"Let it down," he told me. "Let it down. He . . . he can't move."

"What?"

"Let it down," Evan told me in a whisper. "There's a piece of metal . . . it's stuck right into him. We can't. . . ."

Evan was right – we couldn't. There was nothing we could do. If we pulled him out, the metal would slice right through him. As it was, Bill must be bleeding to death. Moving him would just make his blood come out faster.

Did he know that?

I looked down at Bill Kerner, his face wracked with pain. He was dying. Soon it would be all over. There was nothing anyone could do.

"Cyrus. . . ." he cried out.

Then his body shivered, and his eyes seemed to roll

back. A funny sound came from his throat. And then there was no movement at all.

"Is he . . . ?" Evan asked.

"Yeah," I said.

We both looked down at him for a second or two, but there was nothing more we could do. Not for him.

Chapter 9
Searching

We left Bill Kerner's body where it was, then made our way up to the third floor. The stairs led right to the X-Ray Unit – my mom's unit. Of course, the unit does more than X-rays now. There are two CAT machines, and one MRI scanner. There are two rooms for doing ultrasounds. And the doctors must do other things I don't know about.

Or used to do them. Now the whole unit was a wreck. Some walls and chunks of ceiling were down. One big CAT machine was in pieces. The nurses' station was a mess. The ceiling had fallen and smashed it all.

And it was quiet. Unlike the crying and moaning down below, there was no sound.

"Anybody here?" Mr. Wu shouted.

No answer.

I walked down the hallway toward my mom's lab. "Anybody here?" I shouted. Then I had to add, "Mom, are you still here?"

No answer.

Mr. Wu came over to us. "Seems like everybody got out. Cyrus, you and Evan check the rooms. We're going down the hall. If it's all clear, we'll meet you on the fourth floor. Okay?"

"Yeah, sure."

"And keep listening. If we get hit again, you don't want to be under there." He pointed to where the ceiling had fallen on the nurses' station. "Duck and cover. Remember?"

"Just like school," I said.

"Except this is real."

Mr. Wu led the teachers down the hall. I knew the cancer unit was down that way. Surely all those patients could get out by themselves. Or so I thought.

"So your mom got out," Evan said.

"Yeah, looks like it," I replied. I wasn't sure. How could anyone be sure? I had some kind of feeling that my mom was still there. I couldn't explain it. I just felt it.

"So I'll check the rooms on the left, you do the rooms on the right," Evan said.

It seemed like a plan. There were only ten rooms in the unit, and there was no noise so it all seemed easy. Go into a room, look around, shout, listen and then move on.

So we made our way down the hall, over chunks of fallen ceiling, until we got to the end. I went right; Evan went left.

"Anybody here?" I shouted.

No answer. It was the first CAT room. The big machine was at one side, so I took a look inside. Nobody there. Then I looked around the room. Nobody in sight.

"Clear in this room," I shouted to Evan. He was shouting the same thing back to me.

The next room was for X-rays, and there were two parts to it. Nobody on the bed, nobody behind the screen. Clear.

This was going to be easy, I told myself. The next room told the same story – nobody there. But I did hear a shout from Evan across the hall.

"Cy . . . Cy, there's a problem here."

"Yeah?" I shouted, walking that way.

"I . . . I don't know what to do," Evan whispered.

I could smell the problem before I saw it. There was something dead in that room.

I saw where Evan was pointing. It was a leg and a shoe – a man's leg and shoe. The rest of the body was buried under the X-ray tube, a pile of ceiling and fallen wall.

The man was dead. Simple as that.

"Leave him," I said. "Nothing we can do."

Evan shook his head. "But shouldn't we . . . like, check for a pulse?"

"There's no pulse, Evan. He's gone. We're here to help the people who are alive. Remember?"

Evan grunted but didn't move. I left him behind. There was nothing more I could say, but I knew how he felt. I'd never seen a dead body like that. I mean, I've been to funerals, but the bodies are all cleaned up. They hardly look real. But this body was a mess – one look was enough to see that. The leg was twisted. There was blood seeping out on the floor.

It wasn't pretty. Real death never is, I guess.

We got through the next pair of rooms pretty fast. I guess neither of us wanted to look that hard. I mean, maybe we'd find another body – but then what?

My last room was 3W17, another X-ray room – or double room. X-ray rooms are always double rooms. The patient lies down on the table with the X-ray tube overhead. The X-ray tech, sometimes that's my mom, is behind a wall with the controls.

But in this room, the wall had fallen over. There was just a pile of rubble on one side. A mess.

"Anybody there?"

Then I heard something. I didn't know what. Something.

I walked over toward the patient table and called again. "Anybody under here?" Then I looked around. I even lifted the bed, but there was nobody down there . . . or anywhere.

Evan stuck his face in the doorway. "I'm done. What's up here?"

"Don't know," I said. "Just listen."

So the two of us took a moment to listen. From outside, we could hear sirens and motor sounds. From inside there was a drip of water somewhere. And another sound – like air moving in and out. Like breathing.

"Where are you?" I called out. "Can you make a

noise or move something?"

There was a sound, something like a grunt. And then a bump – from the pile of rubble.

Evan and I went over to the pile of rubble – what had been a wall. Now it was a mound of plaster and wires and electric gear.

"There's somebody under there," Evan said.

"Yeah," I agreed. But I was already pulling off the top layer of junk. I tried to be careful. I didn't want to make it worse for the guy down there.

"We'll get to you," I said.

I couldn't tell how badly the person was hurt. But I'd heard a sound, so the person couldn't be dead.

Evan began pulling away chunks of plaster from one side; I worked at the other. In two or three minutes, we'd pulled away half the rubble.

It was Evan who reached the victim first – or part of the victim. He got one foot free. It was a foot in a nurse's white shoe.

"Cyrus," he called to me. "Look."

My heart did this massive thump in my chest. I started digging faster, pulling away plaster and wires like a crazy man. Finally I could see something that looked like flesh. Something. . . .

I pulled away two more chunks of ceiling. Then Evan and I managed to lift a big box of X-ray plates. And there was the victim.

"Mom," I cried.

Chapter 10
More Shocks

Mom was out cold, but she was breathing. I put my ear down to her face and could hear her breathing.

"Is she . . . ?" Evan asked.

"She's alive," I told him. "Breathing seems okay. We just have to get this junk off her, but be careful."

I kept thinking of Bill Kerner. He seemed okay at first, but a piece of metal was stuck right through him. Now maybe that isn't the worst thing. I've seen worse than that on TV – guys with a metal bar right through their brains. They live through it. They come out okay.

But my mom, we just didn't know. She must have been knocked out when the wall fell on her. She probably kept working after the first quake – that's what she is like. But then the aftershock sent the wall down. Maybe the X-ray box hit her head. Maybe a chunk of ceiling. There was no telling. But we had to be careful that there was nothing worse, nothing sticking into her.

So we pulled stuff off her a piece at a time. Evan made a pile beside him; I made one beside me. Slowly we could see more of my mom. She was in her nurse's outfit – kind of green scrubs. There didn't seem to be any blood, at least not on the outside. There was no telling about inside. Internal bleeding is the worst, I've read that.

In five minutes, we had her clear. She was still breathing slowly, like she was asleep. I thought about taking her pulse, but what would be the point?

"Do we move her?" Evan asked. "I mean, if her back's been hurt, we're not supposed to do that."

"Yeah. That's what they say. Leave the victim alone and wait for the ambulance. But you know what?"

"What?"

"We're the ambulance," I said. "We've got to get her out of here, somehow. Can you go find Mr. Wu? Maybe if we got her on a stretcher."

"Yeah, good plan."

"I'll stay with her until you get back. Just in case."

Then Evan was gone, heading down the hall. I looked at my watch – 1:10 in the afternoon. The first quake had been four hours ago. The aftershock about an hour after that. So it had been quiet for about three hours. Maybe it was all over. Maybe we just had to wait for help.

My mom groaned.

"Mom?" I said.

No answer. No more sound. Just breathing.

"Mom, can you hear me?"

No answer.

I looked at my watch. 1:17. Evan should have found Mr. Wu by now. They should be heading back with a stretcher. We'd get mom out of here. The doctors outside would know what to do. She'd be okay.

I even said that out loud. "You'll be okay."

Then I felt the rumble. It was big and it was deep. All around me, things started to move. There were more sounds – glass cracking, things breaking. Then the floor seemed to move under my feet.

So I jumped up to cover my mom's face, and I put my hands over the back of my head to cover me.

Everything was moving again. Things were falling

on the right and left. Then I heard a crack from up above, but I was smart enough not to look up. I kept my head covered and waited.

Then everything went black.

I don't know how long I was out. I do know that I had a hard time getting my eyes open. They seemed to be crusted with dust. But even when my eyes were open, I couldn't see much. There was something like plaster right in front of me, and a little bit of bright light beyond that. But I was so confused. Where was I? What had happened?

When the answers came into my brain, I tried to move. My mother was beneath me and she had to breathe. I had to make a little room so she could get some air. And then I had to get some air, too. It felt like my lungs were coated with dust, just like my eyes.

I tried to twist my body, but I couldn't move much. I was pinned down by something. Something had fallen on my legs, or against my legs. Something was pushing down on my hands and arms.

I turned my head to one side. That much I could

do. Then I arched my back to try to give some room for mom to breathe. That kind of worked.

But I was still buried. Buried alive! That's supposed to be the worst way to die. I was buried alive.

What was on top of me? That was the big question. After the last aftershock, I didn't think there was much more to fall down. Looks like I got that wrong. But maybe I could push up on whatever was pushing down on me. I tried that – my Plan A. I tried to lift my elbows to push up on my hands, but I was too weak.

I need a Plan B, I told myself. So I took one hand off the back of my head and punched it forward. The piece of plaster in front of me moved. I made a fist and hit it again. The plaster cracked. One more hit and I made a hole in the plaster the size of my fist.

Not bad, I told myself. I could see light out there – bright light. It was like daylight was pouring into the X-ray unit. And I knew that wasn't good.

I didn't know if it was smart to move my other hand. That one was still covering my head. It wasn't much protection, but it was something.

So I decided to use my feet. With my right leg, I pushed back. Something moved, and that gave me a little more room. I pushed back again, then I kicked back. My right leg was almost free. I could feel fresh air coming from behind me and rushing out the hole my fist had made.

I did the same thing with my left leg. I kicked harder and faster this time. Pretty soon both my legs were free. But then there was another crash, like something falling. I braced myself. Had I done all this just to be crushed by something I kicked loose?

No. Nothing fell on me . . . on us.

So now both my legs were free. My body could move a little. I could wiggle. And if I could do that, maybe I could wiggle free.

So I took my left hand off my head and put it out front. Now I looked like a swimmer doing a shallow dive. I wiggled a little and pulled myself down. Then I wiggled some more and bent my knees. Nothing on top of me seemed to collapse, so I kept going. At one point, I dragged my hand against a sharp piece of metal. I could feel the metal slicing into me, and then I could smell the blood.

So I pulled away from the metal. I told myself to go slow, dead slow. If it took me half an hour to get free, so what? Maybe some help would come sooner. There was no reason to hurry. Maybe there was no reason to get free, but I had to try. Buried alive might be the worst way to die . . . and I didn't want to die that way.

So I inched my way down. Ever so slowly. I was on my knees, and then half my body was free, and then my chest was clear. At that point, my face was right by my mom's face – and she was still breathing. That was good. And I was still breathing. That was good.

But I couldn't go nuts and pull myself out. Slow, slow, slow, I told myself. I couldn't risk having a pile of rubble fall on my mother.

And then, at last, I was free. I sat on the floor, facing the wall that had trapped me. There was blood still dripping from my right hand. And there was my watch – still on my left wrist.

It was 1:45.

Where was Evan? Where was Mr. Wu? Where was somebody to help us?

Chapter 11

Alive

Slow down and think, I told myself. That's tough for me. I'm an act-first, think-later guy. I know that's kind of stupid, but that's how I am.

But I knew that wouldn't work here. We were in deep trouble, my mom and me. The worst trouble of our lives. If I was smart, maybe we'd both come out alive. Then we'd have stories to tell. We'd be able to tell everybody about the great earthquake, and how we lived through it.

But first we had to live through it.

Look around, I told myself. Figure out where you are and make a plan. I even said the words out loud to make myself listen. When I looked around, I understood the bright light. The outer wall of the X-ray unit had fallen off. The wall that used to be windows, was now nothing . . . just sky. The ceiling overhead was sagging down, but it seemed to be holding. I remembered how this kind of building went up. The central core is made of concrete. The outside walls just bolt onto the floors. They're the weakest part. If we stayed close to the middle – the halls, the stairs – we'd be okay.

But first I had to get my mom free. There was so much rubble piled on top of her, I knew I had to wiggle her out the same way I had done before. I'd have to make an opening, then pull her out sideways.

Good thinking, I told myself. But be careful.

The rubble that had fallen on us had made a kind of stone wall. Like any stone wall, it was pretty solid. But if you take out too many stones, the whole thing falls down. So I had to be careful pulling things away. One piece of plaster, one bit of concrete, and the whole thing could come down. And my mother would be crushed to death.

Slow, slow, slow, I told myself.

I got the easy stuff first. Plaster, that's easy. It's light and it cracks in half. Wires and plastic, that's harder. If

I had a saw or a wire cutter, I could just cut away. But I had nothing – just my hands. Still, my hands were doing a pretty good job . . . a little bit at a time.

After a while, I could see most of my mom. She was flat on her back, like a saint in a church. I ran my hand over her and there was good news. No metal bars sticking into her. No reason I couldn't pull her out.

Except for one concrete block. A concrete block is pretty big and pretty heavy. But it's also very solid. If I pulled out this last block, the whole pile might collapse and then . . . then my mom would be dead.

I tried to jiggle the concrete block. No luck. It was in there solid.

The block was my enemy. But then some voice came into my head, make the enemy your friend. Somebody had said that in class last week.

So suppose I got another concrete block, and used that to prop up the hole at the bottom. And then another at the top. And then if I kind of slid my mom. . . .

So I lifted a couple of concrete blocks from the floor and wedged them at my mom's feet. Then I tried to pull her with one arm, but that didn't work. I tried pulling on the shoulders of her hospital scrubs, but that didn't work. She wasn't stuck. She just wasn't moving. I couldn't get both sides of her to move at once.

Think, I told myself. Then I sat back on the floor. Outside, there were all sorts of noises – sirens and motors and helicopters. But inside, where we were, there was nothing. Nobody was coming. Maybe Evan had never made it out. Maybe Evan was dead himself.

Maybe I was already dead and just flashing through the last minutes of my life.

No, no way.

I remembered something from my life guard course. If a drowning victim is fighting you, don't try to grab his arms. Grab his hair. Right now, my mom wasn't drowning, and she wasn't fighting. But there was too much friction between her and the wall. I need more force to pull her out. And the best way to do that was to pull her hair.

Two good things: my mom is pretty small, and she has long black hair.

One bad thing: if she could feel anything, it would really hurt.

"Sorry, mom," I said to her.

Then I took her hair in my hand, wrapped it around my wrist and pulled.

She groaned . . . and she moved.

Now I could take her hair in both hands. I pulled again, and she moved again. Slowly her head was coming out of the wall. One more pull . . . slowly, slowly . . . and her head was clear. One more pull after that and I could reach her shoulders. And then . . . slowly, slowly . . . I dragged the rest of her out.

The two of us fell to the floor, my mom on top of me.

I could hardly breathe. I looked at the wall in front of us, wondering if it would all collapse now. But no, it didn't. So I dragged my mom by her shoulders back a little. Then tried to come up with another plan.

Plan C was simple – get out of here. Get out of here fast.

It would have been better if I'd had a stretcher. Or a wheelchair. But I had nothing like that. But my mom is pretty small, and I'm in pretty good shape from swimming. So I figured I could carry her.

And I did. I lifted her in my arms, one arm under her legs, one arm under her shoulders. She was a dead weight – and that didn't help. But she wasn't a heavy weight, only about 90 pounds, and that helped a lot.

So I carried her. I ducked under the fallen ceilings.

I stepped over piles of broken plaster and concrete. I squeezed through broken doorways. I went down steps that weren't steps any more.

It was slow going. Every five minutes I had to rest. Sometimes I had to put my mom down to clear away stuff ahead of us. Sometimes, my back felt like it was on fire and my arms felt like they would never lift up again.

But we kept going forward, and down, and forward again. Toward the light. Toward air and light and safety.

And then it was right there. The sky opened up blue and bright. People saw us and started running toward us. My mom got lifted from my arms by people who knew what they were doing.

Then I collapsed on the ground. I fell to my knees. And I cried. I cried because somehow we had come out alive.

Chapter 12
Aftermath

Evan and I went to Bill Kerner's funeral. We had never liked the guy much, but we felt we owed him something. A lot of the kids from school were there. A lot of them were crying, but not me. I'd been through worse, as they say.

Evan really did try to get help that day. He'd made it halfway down the hall when that aftershock hit. The floor shifted, he fell, and then a ceiling panel fell on him. When he finally got up, Mr. Wu had moved on. And when he finally got somebody else to help, it was too late.

I had already stumbled out of the hospital carrying my mother. And somebody took a picture.

Somebody also said that you get fifteen minutes of fame in your life. So I've already had mine. The picture of me carrying my mom made the newspapers and TV all across the world. My uncle in Japan sent me a copy. So did a cousin in Germany. I was famous . . . for a while. I guess it was longer than fifteen minutes, long enough that I made a little money selling my story to some British papers. I was kind of hoping to get on Oprah – my mom would have loved that – but no such luck.

My mom was okay, by the way. Her back wasn't broken, so my carrying her didn't do any damage. Her head was banged up a little, but she got over that pretty quick. She kept telling me that her hair hurt after the rescue. I kept telling her that that is pretty weird.

I guess when she reads this she'll know the truth. So it goes.

I still have a pretty mean scar from where I cut my hand, but that's not much. In our town, 27 people died from the quake. Some were buried in their houses. Some were killed when buildings collapsed. Two people died when they had to be moved from the hospital. One guy died when the highway cracked and he actually drove into the road he was on.

So I have a scar. No big deal.

And I'm a hero – at least to my sister and my mom. Mom keeps telling the story over and over, to anybody who'll listen. How her son risked his life to save hers. I have to leave the room when she tells it. I mean, I'm not all that heroic. I did what I could. I got my sister someplace safe after the first quake. I helped out in a disaster. I found my mom in trouble and got her out of it. No big deal.

Now Evan . . . the hero thing is working for him. The former weird guy is now a star. The funny glasses, the wonky music – it's all become cool. He's the "kid who risked his life." And I'm just the guy who rescued his mother and made a million dollars selling his story.

Well, I didn't make a million dollars.

And Tracy McKinnon still doesn't look at me. She knows I exist (that's a step up) but she still doesn't look at me. Next summer, she's working at Dairy Queen so maybe if I buy a lot of Peanut Buster Parfaits. . . .

No, forget that. I'll write my story instead.

Other HIP Xtreme titles to look for

Hostage

by ALEX KROPP

Rob was just making a bank deposit when the robbers burst in. Soon he's one of six hostages down on the floor, trying to keep the trigger-happy bank robbers from losing control. At the end, Rob is the only hostage left – his life hanging by a thread.

Lost

by SHARON JENNINGS

Rafe Reynolds thought it would be easy to lead a group of kids into wilderness camping. But soon he's lost in the woods with one of the campers. Together they have to deal with everything from bears and broken bones to anger and fist fights. It all threatens their survival.

Overboard

by E.L. THOMAS

An accident at sea leaves Tanner in a lifeboat with his kid sister and a guy he really despises. The survival of the group depends on their working together. But as the hot sun beats down and the water runs out, their chances don't look good.

Wave

by D.M. OUELLET

Luke and Mai could see the tsunami coming at them, but that didn't give them enough time to get away. When the wave hit, they fought to breathe and fought to reach dry land. And that was only the beginning of the disaster.

Alex Kropp is the author of *Hacker* (HIP Sr. series), *Turf War* (HIP Edge series) and *Quake* (HIP Xtreme). He has done editorial work for a number of publishers and now works in product development for Research In Motion.

For more information on HIP novels:

High Interest Publishing
www.hip-books.com

Frozen

by LORI JAMISON

Frank and Ray are stranded in the Arctic. Their plane's snowmobile is broken and no one knows where they are. An Arctic storm is coming that can freeze them to death in minutes. The question is simple: how can they survive?